Wyatt's First W

By Shasta Sitto

Illustrated by Marvin Teeples

MW00896552

Second Edition - 2018
ISBN 978-0-9915571-4-1

Wyatt rushes home from school as quickly as he can. Today is the day his grandpa is taking him deer hunting for the very first time!

Since hunting requires a lot of responsibility, Wyatt had to prove to his parents and his grandpa that he was ready. He did this by taking good care of his dog, completing his hunter safety course, and practicing gun safety.

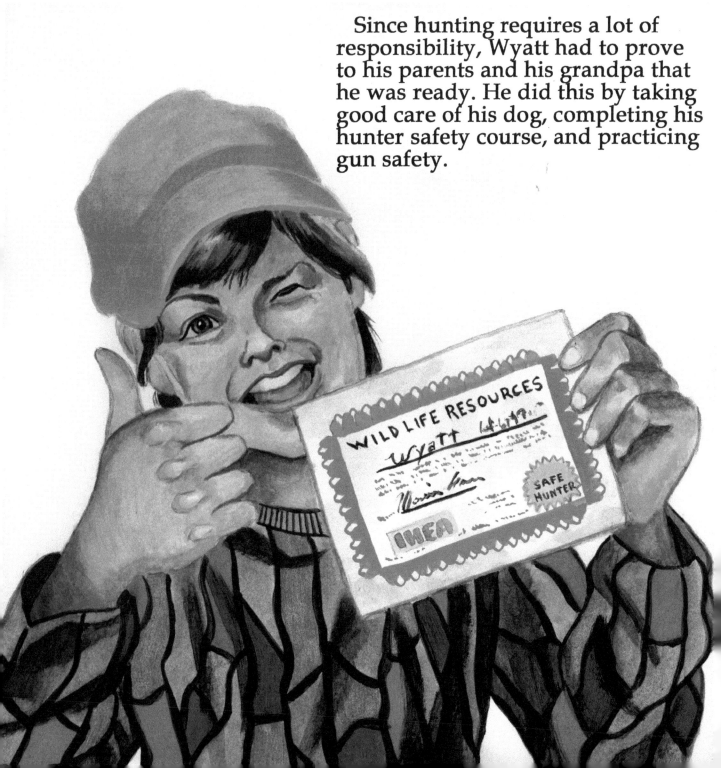

Wyatt runs to his room and quickly puts on his camouflage pants, jacket, and boots. He grabs his binoculars and hat, and dashes to the front yard to find his grandpa waiting for him.

"I'm ready to go, Grandpa!" exclaims Wyatt.

"Not quite," replies Grandpa. "You forgot your orange hunting vest. It's very important to wear orange in the woods so other hunters don't mistake you for an animal."

"Oh yeah!" says Wyatt. He darts back into the house and grabs his orange vest. Now he is ready to go.

Grandpa loads Wyatt's gun case safely into his truck. They climb in and head to the woods.

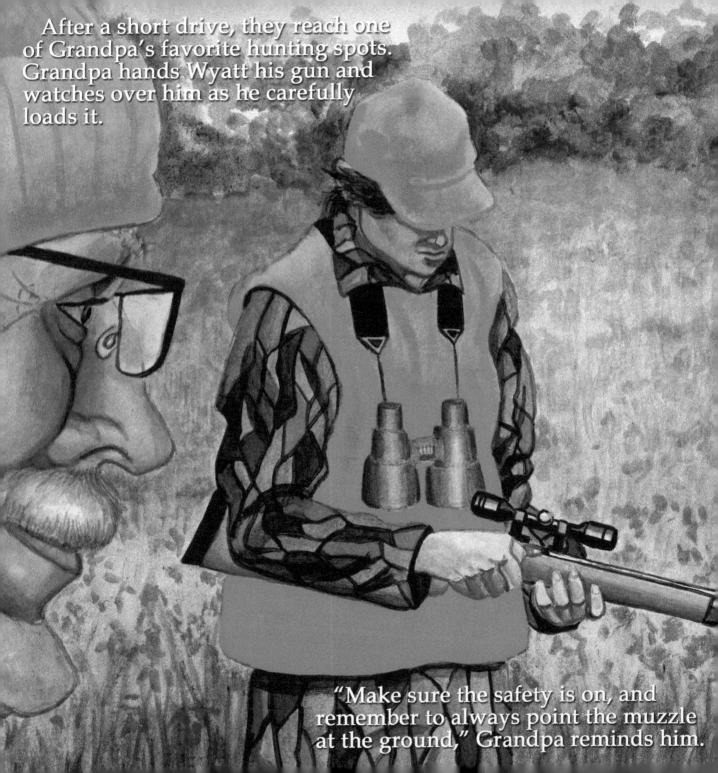

After a short drive, they reach one of Grandpa's favorite hunting spots. Grandpa hands Wyatt his gun and watches over him as he carefully loads it.

"Make sure the safety is on, and remember to always point the muzzle at the ground," Grandpa reminds him.

"Ok, we're ready to hunt," Grandpa says with a smile. "Remember to be as quiet as you can while we walk so that we don't scare any deer away. Let's go!"

After walking for a short time, Wyatt
looks to his right and spots a deer.
   "Grandpa, there's a deer!" Wyatt
whispers excitedly. "It's huge! Let's go
get it!"

"Hold on, Wyatt," replies Grandpa. "That is a nice buck, but we have to let it go. See that fence between the buck and us? It's on somone else's property, and we don't have permission to hunt there."

Wyatt is disappointed, but knows how important it is to follow the rules. They keep walking.

Soon they come to a
pretty creek lined with trees.
"This is a good spot," says Grandpa.
"We'll sit right here with the wind
blowing toward us so that it won't
carry our scent to the deer and scare
them away."

They sit, and sit, and sit some more. At first, Wyatt is excited. He keeps his eyes peeled for any sign of deer. But as time drags on, he gets bored, and begins playing with an ant that is crawling on his boot.

Suddenly, out of the corner of his eye, Wyatt sees a flash of red. He looks up to see a fox walking near the creek.

"Grandpa, there's a fox!" Wyatt whispers as he points toward the creek. "Can I shoot it?"

"No, Wyatt," Grandpa replies. "We only have a deer tag, and it's not right to kill animals that you don't have a tag for. Plus, firing the gun would scare away any deer that might be close."

Wyatt enjoys watching the fox as it gets a drink and runs back into the trees.

Wyatt's grandpa taps him on the shoulder and points to the line of trees on the other side of the creek. A doe is walking out of the trees and more are following her.

They watch doe after doe emerge from the trees until, finally, a buck steps out. It's not as big as the buck they saw earlier in the day, but it's beautiful.

Wyatt decides that this is his buck. He looks at his grandpa to make sure it's ok to shoot. His grandpa gives him a thumbs up.

Wyatt's hands shake a little as he raises his gun and takes the safety off. He tries to stay calm as he finds the buck through his scope. He aims at the spot behind the shoulder blade. He takes a deep breath and slowly exhales as he squeezes the trigger. BANG!!!

Wyatt sees the buck
jump and run into the trees.
He leaps up and starts to follow,
but his grandpa stops him.

"Slow down there, pal. You
made a great shot. Let's give the
buck some time. If we scare him,
he'll just run further away."
They only wait a few minutes,
but to Wyatt it seems like a
lifetime. Finally, Grandpa says,
"Ok, let's go find it!"

They begin walking and find the buck a few dozen yards into the trees. Wyatt sees that the buck is dead, and suddenly feels overwhelmed with emotions; excitement from the hunt, pride in his shot, and sadness that the beautiful animal is dead.

Wyatt says a silent thank you to the buck for giving its life to feed him and his family. He then looks up at his grandpa, who is smiling from ear to ear.

"Congratulations, Wyatt," says Grandpa. "You took your time, and made a great shot. I'm so proud of you."

"Thank you for taking me hunting, Grandpa," Wyatt replies. "This is the best day of my life."

A few days later, Wyatt, his grandpa, and the rest of the family, sit down to a dinner of venison steak from his buck. Wyatt feels proud that he was able to provide food for his family. He can't wait to go hunting again.

The End.

My Hunting Story

Place a photo here of your first hunting trip, and write your story below.

_____

_____

_____

_____

_____

_____

CPSIA information can be obtained
at www.ICGtesting.com
Printed in the USA
BVHW021450120821
614281BV00019B/998

9 780991 557141